New Day........

So I have decided to write a diary! I do this every year and get to about the third week and then give up, but not this time. I am going to see it through for a whole year!

I have had the worst ever journey getting to work, first I got up late (getting from the south coast to London is going to be a nightmare now at the time I get going).

Secondly, the shirt I was going to wear today had a bloody stain on it so I did the worst thing possible and fished out yesterday's shirt from the wash bin (bit damp smelling but a bit of spray will mask that). Thirdly, this meeting has to go well as I need to hit my sales target. Sat waiting in this dark tiny waiting area that has no windows, pretty grim really, for my customer to have a meeting on a hot August day. I decide today's the day, so here goes.......

August

Friday 6th

Sitting here waiting for people, why? I emailed my customer over two week ago about arranging our meeting for today at midday and they replied, '*Fine with us, see you then.*' They then email me saying, '*Sorry to mess you around, can we make it 12.20pm?*' and I replied, '*Fine with me, see you then*!' It's gone 12.30pm. I am one of those people that hate waiting, especially when it's due to the incompetence of my customers. I like to have enough time to get to other customers in good time, so I can relax and go over what I am going to talk about before each appointment. It's now 12.40pm (getting a bit miffed now). Sat here twiddling my thumbs and noticing that my nails need re-polishing, chipped nail varnish is not a good look. I began to wish I was at home starting on my book, dreaming of that amazing life I have always wanted for my boyfriend Graham, my cat Bongo and me, to have a camper van and drive around the world).

I notice a local map on the wall (it's now 12.52pm), amazed by the names of the places. I start to direct each one:

(DORK)ING- *I feel like one sitting, here*

LEATHERHEAD-*my head does feel like a piece of leather old, worn and used*

(VIRGIN)IA WATER- *well there are not many in this place by the looks of it. They are either pregnant or like a cake or two.*

EGHAM- *ohhhhhhh I am hungry (now 1pm)*

FELT (HAM) - *Yep I am definitely getting a ham and egg sandwich for lunch (if I*

ever get out of here)

GUILD(FORD)-*not far from home :(*

(HAM)PTON- *God, I am so hungry, hurry up will you! (Now 1.05pm)*

(TAD)WORTH- *I am a tad pissed off now, I am still waiting and it's now 1.10pm.*

(GOD)STONE- *God, hurry up!*

(PUR)LEY- O*h, I miss my cat. I wish I was at home snuggled up with a nice cuppa and lunch with my Bongo.*

(BARK)ING- *I'm barking mad waiting this long*

(CAR)SHALTON- *I should just go to my car and leave they are so pushing their luck the stupid fuc........*

"Oh, good afternoon, Jane! So sorry to have kept you. How are you? You haven't been waiting long, have you?"

"Oh no, of course not. Don't be silly," I reply. Why did I just lie? I should have said, "In fact yes, I have. It's now 1.15pm. I have wasted forty-five minutes of my life waiting in this mothball-scented dingy little waiting room that really reminds me of a bus shelter at the end of my mum and dad's road, made of wood, no windows, smelling a lot like dogs' wee, I have had no cup of coffee offered to me whilst I wait, and no update as to where the hell you were, so now I am leaving. Goodbye!"

Saturday 7th

Whenever I see an offer, I need to be involved.

Today I went into my local bookshop and spotted a great deal; buy one book and get one half price, what a bargain! I bought four and saved five pounds, doesn't seem that much of a saving now, but at the time I was really chuffed. I wouldn't have even bought the books if the offer sign wasn't hanging in the window calling to me. The funny part was at the counter. "Do you want a bag with this?" asked the spotty teenage, chewing gum (which actually looked like she was chewing her own tongue). I think to myself, '*Well yes, you idiot!*' but instead reply, "Oh yes please, thank you."

"That will be one penny for the bag," grunted the sarcastic, tongue-chewing teenager.

"Yes, fine. I usually say keep the change, so I'll just have a bag this time." As I put my bargain purchases into my one penny bag, I notice the women next to me at the other checkout had the same question asked and she says, "Yes, please." The young cashier girl, who looked a lot more presentable than the cashier I had, then said, "OK, we charge a penny for each bag. Is that OK?" With that the women replied, "Oh, don't bother then! I pay my taxes and then I get charged for a plastic bag!"

What is wrong with these people? It's only a penny, for goodness sake!

I still think that plastic bags should be banned though. We should all use cloth bags, it's so much better for the environment and a good way of disguising where you have been shopping!

Sunday 8th

Went to my mum and dad's today, to get the back of my

legs waxed by my mum (holy shit! how much does that hurt?) The last time I had this done was when I was eighteen and drunk, (that was a few years back now and have erased this part of my life from my brain!) Mum reminds me that it's Nan's birthday tomorrow. (Oh shit, I forgot again! Every year I do this. I must put it on the calendar). One hour later, my thighs bright red and blotchy from the dreaded waxing (glad I didn't do the bikini line), I hobbled into town to buy Nan a helium balloon (what an earth possessed me to buy that? She's not five!), a good old box of chocolates (all of her twelve grandchildren get her a box), yellow lilies (God, it's not her funeral!) and a fridge magnet shaped as a heart which says, 'Grandchildren keep you young' (not sure she would agree!). Anyway, when I went round to her house to present these wonderful gifts, the smile quickly disappeared when I saw what gifts others had got her. We all had the same idea! Need to think of some better gifts next year, her fridge couldn't physically take any more magnets after this year.

After my visit to Nan, I went round to my friend Sarah's mum and dad's (she still lives at home).Whilst I was round there, I felt very uncomfortable. You could have cut the tension in the air with a knife. Sarah's dad was having a drink (or two) and offered her mum a sherry. After downing her sherry and slamming it on the table like she was having a drinking competition, she brought up the fact that she would be going out for lunch the following day for her birthday. Sarah's dad muttered under his breath, "Thanks, I'll just stay at home then." To my amazement, Sarah's mum heard her husband's slurred sarcastic comment and clucked back at him, "Well you can come, only if you promise to behave yourself and not get drunk, as I can't be doing with looking after you on my special day." Sarah's dad looked a little shocked with this reaction and then muttered, "I would rather stay at home anyway!

That way I won't bother anyone and then I can do my own things." "What like watching the football? Drinking? Making the place look untidy? Burping and farting?".... And I made a quick exit to Sarah's bedroom. I have never seen them bicker like this before. It made me realise that having a drink gives you courage to say things you may not say when totally sober. It doesn't matter how new or old a relationship is, it is the same.

Love, arguments, history, future! My dad always said to me, "Drink is the worst drug, it always starts up an argument."

Monday 9th

I went shopping today and bought our flavoured tea bags and saw some slimming ones and thought I would give them a go; a) because it had the word 'slimming' on them and b) because they have fennel in them so should be tasty!

I was wrong on both. It tasted like the smell of a Grow Bag mixed with the taste of the end of a biro you've sucked and realised ink has got into your mouth. The box states that the slimming tea bag ‘lowers the appetite’. They are not wrong there, I think it may have something to do with that fact it makes you want to puke. That is one pound eighty-nine pence I definitely won’t be spending again. Back to fruit and exercise, just think I could have bought a hundred and eighty-nine bags from the book shop!

Friday 13th

Graham, his son Jack, Jack's friend Bret and I have gone away to Devon for a long weekend. So I have decided that I will only write in the diary when something happens or makes me want to write, that way I don’t have to punish myself for not writing in it some days!

Day Two of our holiday: feeling really relaxed (even though my neck aches, back aches, have puffy eyes and feel a cold coming on due to the fact we are staying in a tent; the description was 'two man tent', they must have been very, very skinny men).

I promised myself and my boyfriend that I would turn my work phone off and leave it at home for a stress free holiday. At about one p.m. we were lying on the beach (a locals' hideaway not far from Land's End), and along came a family of about twelve who sat in front of us in the sand. I looked up, I saw that the father of the family was wearing a fleece with the logo of where I worked. Typical! You can go to the very end of the country and you either see somebody you know or something to do with your Work. When will those bloody lottery numbers come up? It's my time to win, surely?

Saturday 14th

Well the time is now seven a.m., it has been raining all night and is now starting to come through the tent. We have decided to leave this morning, as the weather is not going to improve; bloody miserable, like the kids!

Why is it when you pack up and load the car before your holiday, it all fits in lovely and neat but when you pack up to leave, it doesn't all fit? I even threw away the tents and deck chairs, and we had eaten all the food we bought, so there must be room?!

I am writing this whilst in the car, the kids are covered in bags and I have a cooker hob thing, bag, wash bag, various hats and the road map in between my legs, and we still have four hours and ten minutes before we get home....

We are now back home. Isn't it funny, when you go away somewhere you always say to each other, 'wouldn't it be nice if we could give everything up and move here?' So that night I spent hours on the internet looking for houses and businesses in the Land's End area.

I came up with the following ideas:

1. Buy a caravan, leave our jobs and live like travelers (which has always been a secret dream of mine, I like the romance of it).

2. Make an income by teaching people to surf (even though we can only body-board and have only been doing that for a week).

3. Set up and run a lovely bed and breakfast. How lovely that would be, to own a lovely house to share with others, we could have chickens to lay the eggs for our guests at breakfast, have a small allotment to grow fruit and vegetables. I could even bake bread as well (even though the last bread loaf I made looked like road kill and I have not made it since).

I have spoken to Graham about my ideas and he likes them, by that I mean he grunted appropriately when I mentioned it, so I am assuming this means he is one hundred per cent in agreement with me, despite the golf being on, and him being totally focused on the TV.

Thursday 19th

"Let's go back to Cornwall on our own. I want to learn how to surf," I say to Graham. He agreed and bought a pink surf board for me (a bargain at ninety pounds for a second hand foam board). I also *had* to get matching bikini, hoodie, two matching t-shirts, a matching dress and matching shorts, there was a sale on, 'buy one get one free', and we did save seventy-five pounds!

Friday 20th

We have ended up in Croyde, North Devon, at a camp site where Graham had stayed at a few years back. When we arrived, the guy at reception (which was actually a shed with a slot cut out for him to serve from) said, "That's fifteen pounds fifty per person per night!" I thought my boyfriend had been sick a little bit in his mouth by the look on his face. So I jumped in and said, "Oh we only have a card. We will just go to a cashpoint and be back." I know it's cheaper than a hotel, but bloody hell, I only want to camp and use about ten feet by ten feet of their field! With that, the boy from the shed said, "We do take cards, so don't worry about going back into town." I didn't know what to say apart from demanding my boyfriend to put his foot on it and we sped off. We finally ended up in a site down the road for a bargain price of eight pounds per person per night. We had the pick of the site, so we chose the pitch at the top of the hill. The views were amazing. Sitting above everyone else on the field, we noticed how people flock like sheep, by how close they all pitch together. It's as though they feel safer being closer. I thought being on the top was a brilliant idea, until it pissed it down and the shower/toilet block was at the bottom of the hill, which caused me a problem as I am scared of the dark, so I had to go for a wee outside the van, which is not my idea of comfort.

After our last camping disaster, we moved on from a two man tent and are now camping in the work van that has been cleaned out and has our blow-up mattress in. I have used the cupboards for our clothes and bags, the food and cooker are on the shelf behind the seats, and the new surf boards are above where we are sleeping, held up by netting. Not quite the camper van I dream of owning one day, but it is so much better than a tent!

Sunday 22nd

Walking to the washing facilities, when we said hello to one of our camping neighbours, who was remarkable like Quasimodo with his strange voice, strange tic and strange stoop (so Graham and I named him Quazzy). He was telling us how he decided to take his kids camping in

Cornwall rather than their annual trip to France. I bet his kids hate him for this, it has been nonstop rain since they arrived.

In the evening when we were walking passed Quazzy's tent, Graham nudged me and pointed discreetly and we had our little joke about Quazzy. He actually was a really sweet man, about five minutes later he walked straight past us, we didn't realise he was walking towards us when we were doing the impressions of him!

Monday 23rd

Quazzy didn't even look at us when we left, I felt so bad, as he really was a nice guy and he was saying what a lovely couple we were. I think I should go to confess my sins. I am such a horrible person. As we drove out of the campsite I thought to myself, *I hope we have not ruined his holiday*.

Tuesday 24th

Why is it that when you're stuck in traffic when going on holiday, it's fun? But when you are stuck in traffic for work because of a sodding camper van breaking down on the motorway, and they shut every lane but one to clear it, it's not fun? I am stuck in traffic as I write this, on the motorway on my way to work. Holiday weeks go too quickly, working weeks don't, FACT!

Saturday 28th

My boyfriend's dad just told us the police are outside, "probably coming to raid the house." I just laughed, wondering what idiot has been up to no good. You will never believe what happened next. I just finished washing up dinner plates and pans after cooking a pasta dish with salmon, mushrooms, cucumber, tomatoes, olive oil, lemon juice and basil, in a trademark dish I cook call 'salmon surprise' (to make it sound posh), but basically it's all the leftovers in the fridge.

BANG BANG BANG. "It's probably the police coming to take me away for my dodgy dinner," I joked to myself. Graham just looked at me blankly.

"Hello, what do you lot want?" Graham's dad said to the four heavily armed police stood at the door.

"We are here about the kayak, it was put up for sale registered to this address."

"What about it?"

Even though I had *never* done anything wrong, you still over-think things in your head, thinking, *have I done anything I shouldn't have?*

"We need to speak to a Miss Wooey."

"Miss Whoey?" he asked, puzzled.

"Miss Wooey."

"That's me," I say, emerging from the kitchen.

"No need to panic," they say, (a bit late for that as there was now four of them stood heavily armed in my living room. To cut a long story short, apparently they had a call from a shop down the road in the town I live, claiming that a kayak that I had up for sale online was identical to the one they had stolen from them twenty-four hours ago (and I listed it online twenty-four hours ago). I was relieved to know that I was not going to be arrested, as the serial number did not match and I still had the receipts from when I bought mine.

September

Tuesday 7th

Every bloody Tuesday I always do it, I even said to my boyfriend, *I am not doing it any more.* But I just can't control myself.

Every Tuesday I treat myself to magazines. I end up buying six different ones that all have the same stories but a different start, middle and ending.

For example, one magazine will say so and so have split up, another one would say they have got married, and another will say they died. I think I buy them to make me realise how normal I am, and how lucky I am to have my life. The magazines come to about seven pounds twenty-four a week (that's seven hundred and twenty-four bags in the local bookshop).

Wednesday 8th

I was on my way back from a busy day at work (stuck on the M25 for most of it). Near my house is one of those two lane roads that merges into one lane, this is a tricky one as I am always on the correct side (left hand side), where you patiently wait in the queue, cursing all the clever people in the right hand lane merging in (only the people who don't mind an argument and being called a prick go in that lane). Well, today I decided to be one of those clever pricks as I had been stuck in traffic all day, and as my house is on this road, so I AM ALLOWED. I got near to where the lanes merge (I felt like I was driving down the green mile) but no one was letting me in. They started to straddle both lanes so I couldn't get in, so I tooted at the person in front of me and pointed to the sign that states they merge in turn. By doing this, I got the middle finger and called a 'stupid bitch' by a lovely mother with her two children in the car, what a charming role model those children have to look up to.

Thursday 9th

We have a couple of lodgers at our house, Leanne and Andrew. Andrew is such a gentle giant but looks like a hard bastard (I also treat him as my son, which is a tad strange as he is ten years older than me). He farts, burps, sings all the time, whistles and likes to lie naked on his bed during the daytime on top of his duvet with his bedroom door wide open. I only know this as I went upstairs to put my boyfriend's clean clothes away in his wardrobe. NEVER AGAIN. Well, the story here is when I moved Bongo, my cat in, (bless him), he was very inquisitive and we told everyone in the house that he couldn't go outside for two weeks and to make sure doors and windows were kept shut if he was in that room. So

Bongo wanders upstairs and was creeping around, when all of a sudden I heard crash-bang-wallop and Bongo came bolting down the stairs with his fur standing on end! I found out that my lodger caught the sight of Bongo and realised his window was open (he lives on the third floor, long drop) leapt naked from his bed and slammed the window. Poor Bongo has not been up there since.

Saturday 11th

We played in an online poker tournament this evening against another three hundred and sixty online players, (something called a free roll). First prize was three hundred pounds, second prize was two hundred pounds, third prize was one hundred pounds and fourth place was eighty pounds, and so on.

It started at seven p.m., and by eleven p.m. we were in the last ten players list. It was all too exciting for me, so I cut up a melon to celebrate (it was too late to open the wine, and it was a week night). We ended up coming fourth, which was fantastic, so I suggested that we gave up work and did this for a living whilst running our dream bed and breakfast. By the look on my boyfriend's face, I should just stick to my boring day job and try and finish writing my book.

Tuesday 14th

Went on a course at work today .Talk about teaching us to suck eggs!! What are these courses all about? Instead of wasting money on these useless courses, couldn't they give us a pay rise instead? You'd get a better workforce then! The trainers for these courses have no clue, and are stuck in the seventies with their textbook teaching methods. What makes me laugh is that usually I have porridge for breakfast, a sandwich for lunch and then dinner when I get home. But when I am on a course I always seem to have about seven quarter sandwiches, a bag of crisps, (a banana so I don't feel so bad), the lonely muffin that's been left all on its own, one of those weird curry battered pyramid things (what the hell are those things anyway?). I think I eat all this as it's free and it seems a shame to waste it. I couldn't stop laughing in the course today, as a colleague of mine challenged the trainer with a question that he couldn't answer. He should have just said he didn't know, but he tried to answer it and made himself look like a right pillock and then said, "Has that answered your question?" It's madness. I wonder how much he gets paid for teaching us absolutely nothing?

Wednesday 15th

I phoned up to cancel one of those credit checks companies today. After being on hold for fifteen minutes, I was then transferred to a Barry Smith (who had a very strong Indian accent) and then had to go through some checks to make sure it was me; i.e. my name, age, password, mother's maiden name and address. He might as well have asked for my bust, hips and waist measurements whilst he was at it. When I told him I was calling to cancel his reply was, "Oh, Mrs. I am so sorry to hear you want to leave," he actually sounded like he was about to cry. I felt so guilty. I replied, "Yes, I am sorry I want to leave, I no longer need it. The free trial was great, I got what I needed." He replied "But, Mrs. did you know for two ninety-nine per month you can get free protective alerts to your phone?" I replied, "No, as I said, I no longer need it." He replied, "But, Mrs. did you know for one ninety-nine you can get free email alerts?" I replied, "No, as I said, I no longer want the service." God, will he just give up? How can it be free if it's a monthly charge? He replied, "But, Mrs...." I hung up, bored and annoyed with his sales pitch!

Thursday 16th

Not happy today. Just got an email from my boss to say I won't be getting my bonus as there are new criteria I have to meet now. What the hell! I have worked so bloody hard this year, done so much extra to help out, secured a lot of new and existing business for them, and they can't even pay me a few hundred pounds bonus?

The day I finish writing my book and get it published, I will be loving it, as I will be working for myself and rewarding myself with the bonuses (probably shoes and bags) I deserve for doing a bloody good job!

Friday 17th

One of the bosses at work was in need of a Word document and I saved it in a folder called 'Misc Corres.' So I told her that this would be in the group file.

"Corry as in Coronation Street?" she asked.

“No, why on earth would I name a file after Coronation Street? 'Corres' stands for correspondence,” I explained.

“OK then, missed?” she said.

“Ah?” I ask.

“Missed.”

I wondered, “Missed what?”

“You said missed. Why would you make a file if it’s been missed?” she asked.

“What the hell are you going on about?” I asked, slightly irritated by this point.

“You said 'Missed Corry',” she spluttered.

“No, I said 'MISC' as in 'miscellaneous'!”

Why do we think that abbreviations save time? How on earth these people are in management, I’ll never understand. I'm beginning to wonder that what’s been said about her, that she slept with one of the directors is true, because she is so bloody thick.

The other day this same person was asked if she wanted a coffee and how she had it, her reply was "black, white and no sugar"; everyone in the room went quiet and just laughed. She didn't understand why everyone was laughing, so the person asked her to repeat herself, so she did and everyone laughed and she still didn't get it. So it was explained to her that it didn't make sense what she said, so she got quite angry and said, "Yes it does coffee is black in colour, milk is white in colour and I don't have sugar" - amazing.

Saturday 18th

A new saying I am going to remember forever, "*never worry what people think about you, let them worry about what you think about them.*"

Sunday 19th

We went to view a beautiful chocolate-box style cottage

today in a lovely village in Surrey. We have fallen in love with it, but guess what? We are in a chain so it could take ages and apparently there is a cash buyer who has already put an offer on it and are ready to move in! How dare people have so much money that they can buy a house outright (I do wonder if estate agents just tell you that so you feel you have to put a good offer in)! It is a really lovely property, so maybe if (when) I get my book finished I will be able to buy my house outright too!

Wednesday 22nd

Why am I addicted to stationery? I see a set of pens or pads (anything bright or pink) or in fact anything, I will buy it. I could open my own stationery shop, it's a joke. I am writing this in one of my new pens (it makes my writing look all neat like an English teacher's). Graham thinks it's sad!

Thursday 23rd

Why, when you ask someone NOT to do something, do they do it? For example, we told one of our lodgers, Leanne (who in fact has the tidiest room and is a little OCD about it) that our house is up for sale and we need to keep it clean, tidy and clutter-free. So my boyfriend and I cleaned the house top to bottom (this is a three floor, four bedroom place so it was not a quick job) and it looked lovely when we finished. Since we have cleaned it, Leanne keeps leaving her work bags, computer and folders on the bloody landing, so we keep moving it all and putting it under her bed so she would get the HINT. She still has not got that hint, so I have given up.

Saturday 25th

Karma! Leanne had a bit of a shock this morning whilst eating her breakfast before work. Bongo decided to use his cat litter tray (which is covered, but we have removed the flap as he wouldn't use it otherwise) and he did the most disgusting, smelliest poo I have ever known any living creature do. Leanne had to eat the rest of her breakfast outside because she was nearly sick from the stench!

Monday 27th

Fallen in love with another property, I have sent him a link to show him, I hoped he would like it. My boyfriend hates the property I fell in love with, so I need to get back on the internet and search for somewhere else. It is so stressful looking for a house, I don't wish it on anyone. I just want a house to call home!

Tuesday 28th

Oh my God, I drove for about half an hour today and thought how the bloody hell did I get here? I have done this quite a lot, I think I need take a holiday, maybe I am stressed?

Thursday 30th

Went to view a property after work today, my boyfriend said, "It is a lovely cottage with loads of potential." We got there and it was nothing like the photos, there was very little potential and it was on a major busy road. We hated it!

October

Saturday 2nd

We found a house today that we love so much. We made an offer straight away and the vendors have accepted it. Now they need proof we are in a chain, but the problem we have is the estate agents we are using are a bunch of cowboys, very unhelpful and never there when you need them. They all dress in shiny nylon suits, cheap shoes, flashy fake watches (I am in sales by the way, and I am nothing like this). Stereotypical salesmen who don't know their arses from their elbows.

Anyway I got an itchy right hand today, which is meant to mean I will come into some money! Well, can this hurry up so I can buy this house outright and cut out these middlemen?

Sunday 3rd

I was waiting for Graham to pick me up from town today and decided to sit in the bus shelter and noticed all the graffiti. Apparently *'lola woz ere'*, *'Barry loves cock'*, *'if you want hot sex then call 07**3542***'* I couldn't read the numbers, somebody had scribbled over them and looks like they pointed an arrow at the sentence and written *'and ur mum'*. Nice; hurry up, Graham!

Monday 4th

I have quite a number of customers that I look after, and there is one who thinks they are my only customer! I get demands, sorry I mean emails, about five times a day demanding something or other that needs doing within the next hour or that day. Even when my email states I am away from the office, on a course or on holiday, they seem to think I will answer their email straight away, and if I don't, they act like a child by not putting my first name on the email and changing what once said *'kind regards'* with just their name. Sometimes I just wish that I could send an email back telling them to bugger off.

Thursday 7th

We are now staying put, thanks to the bloody housing market. Mind you, I am glad in a way, as our house is beautiful, even though it needs a bit more TLC.

Friday 8th

I'm one of those people that doesn't believe in superstition, but I always salute magpies.

(I do that thing when you're in your car and you pretend to scratch your head to salute so people don't think you're saluting).

Today I saw about six of them in different locations and couldn't be bothered, thinking to myself that it's a load of rubbish anyway. Then today my skirt has ripped beyond repair (either I have put weight on or the bloody magpies are to blame). A customer of mine needed to see me urgently, so I had to visit them in a pair of workmen's trousers and stiletto heels (either the client did really need to see me or the magpies thought it would be funny to make them ring me, because it really was not that important, I could have dealt with it over the phone). I am going to salute all magpies from now on.

Saturday 9th

We have one of those cars that has those brilliant lights that turns the full beams on when you need them, and turn themselves back to normal lights when it detects any other vehicle. The car is new, so the lights are very bright (I think they have the blue tint) so people constantly flash me and give me the wanker sign as though I have left my lights on full to annoy them. I hope those idiots forget to salute a magpie today.

I really do love these lights, but I think I may have just blinded a cyclist, my car didn't detect them so the lights stayed on full beam. Sorry, cyclist!

Tuesday 12th

Is it me, or do you feel like you are talking to a brick wall with your other half sometimes? I do. I just read him an extract from my book that I am writing, and he just grunted and then started stating how crap the adverts were on television, ignoring me completely. I went on to say, "Do you think my boobs look big in this bra that I am only wearing and nothing else?" His head turned immediately and he said, "That's just cruel not funny, why would you say that and not actually be doing that?"

MEN.

Thursday 14th

Don't you just love it when you go out to eat, and you have a pudding you know you can cook better yourself? Just avoid looking at the price, as you will see it is too expensive and you'll be sitting there working out how many ingredients you could have bought with it, and how many puddings you could have made.

Saturday 23rd

When I go Christmas shopping I can't help but buy myself things. It's terrible, you see so many nice things! I make myself feel better by telling myself that I have bought so many things for others, I deserve a gift (not sure my boyfriend would agree).

Sunday 24th

Bless, my cat is so sweet. He has this biscuit barrel upstairs which his treats are kept in every night (sorry, every minute of the day) he sits next to it and meows for treats.

We ran out of his treats the other day, so when he was out I filled it with Go Cat and he now thinks these are treats. He can't believe his luck that he gets ten treats instead of four now!

Thursday 28th

Why is it when you need to get up early it's too easy to sleep through your alarm and you feel like crap, but the time you forget to turn your phone off when you have a day off, you wake up to it and DINK, you're awake? I wonder if this is the workings of those damn magpies? The other thing I have noticed is, when you do wake up late you can get washed, dressed, do your hair and your make-up in all of ten minutes, but when you are getting ready to go out you need at least two hours and that is still not enough time!

Friday 29th

I am a pretty social person, but when I get my haircut, I feel as if that's what they should focus on. I mean, the conversations we have are boring and 'samey'. My hairdresser assumes you know who they are gossiping about. I did start to bring magazines in, but she just read the bloody stories over my shoulder and was commenting on them before I had even finished the story myself, so I brought my book in today and she still would not get the hint and shut up. I think I need to find a
new hairdresser.

I wonder what she says to other people about me, as I have heard some stories about some people in my town!

Sunday 31st

I always swore I would never own a pair of those furry boots that look like bear feet, but I am afraid I bought a pair and OMG they are the most comfy boots I have ever owned. I can't believe I waited so long for these beautiful beds for feet!

There are, however, these clog-like jelly shoes that I promise I will NEVER own, they are by far the most disgusting things of all time to put on your feet, and in my view a man in a pair should not be trusted.

NOVEMBER

Saturday 6th

Can someone please explain to me why or what happens to your socks when you wash them? Every time I do a wash load, a bloody sock goes missing!

I have now resorted to wearing odd socks just to confuse my washing machine.

Graham must think I am such a tramp, not only do I now wear odd socks, I also own a selection of discolored bras and knickers - very attractive!

Sunday 7th

I don't know why I do this, but if I knock my left hand on something I have to then knock my right hand so it's fair. It's like sometimes I have to turn the lights on and off a couple of times so it's fair, which will ensure then nothing bad will happen. I always have to triple check that I locked the back door and if I am out at somebody else's house and I use their toilet, I have to check I have flushed and I have not dropped paper on the floor. I walk out of that bathroom then enter again for another check over, even though *I know* I have already done this. Is this a sign of OCD or am I just going nuts?

Thursday 11th

Everyone kept saying my car needed a wash, so I did it all it by myself, and I am very proud of this fact. Then five minutes later a seagull decided to pelt my lovely clean car with its very own berry-mixed poo. I would understand if it was a magpie, but a bloody seagull? These are the reasons why I am never cleaning my car again:

1. My arms start to ache when I have started to shammy the bloody thing (and you have to do it otherwise the car goes all smeary).

2. When I finish shammying the car it needs washing again, as I make it all smeary!

3. It costs a small fortune to buy all the cleaning supplies, it's cheaper going to a car wash.

4. I always end up looking like I have been swimming with my clothes on.

5. It always rains an hour later (even in the summer).

6. A bird shits on my car directly after.

Saturday 13th

Because I am blonde, I get blonde jokes thrown at me now and again at work. I may be blonde, but I am far from thick, I know plenty of girls with brown hair and black hair that are thick and bimbo-like.

Today a girl in the office today said the most ridiculous thing, and I wished everybody
was there to hear it, as this is blonder than you can ever get. She said to a disgruntled customer, "I am sorry,

madam, but I will not let you physically abuse me on the phone." Love it. I did think about explaining to her it is impossible to be physically abused over the phone, but I thought better of it (it would take me ages and I didn't have time).

Sunday 14th

I did have to laugh today. I went into town and wanted to try on some clothes, so the girl in the shop gave me six tokens for my six items (they give you these so they can make sure you don't nick anything). By the time I had tried all the clothes on that clearly had the wrong sizes sewn into the labels (I AM A SIZE TEN), got all hot and bothered, static hair and sweaty body, I went to give in my six items and my six tokens, but the girl had disappeared and left a sign up stating '*lunch break - please place unwanted items on rail and tokens back in token cubby hole!*' What's the point? That's a robber's dream!

Wednesday 17th

Cold weather and newly shaven legs! Not, I state *not,* a good look. Chicken legs, enough said.

Friday 19th

OMG I am so livid, I got taxed over a thousand pounds this month as I have worked my butt off to smash my target. I went into town to cheer myself up with a bit of retail therapy, and to my disgust I hear these skanky people complaining they don't get enough benefits from the government. WELL GET OF YOUR FU**ING ARSES AND GET A JOB, DON'T GIVE ME CRAP THAT "THERE AIN'T NONE" BECAUSE THERE ARE PLENTY, BUT YOU ARE TOO PIG HEADED TO PICK FROM FIELDS OR TOO HIGH AND MIGHTY TO CLEAN TOILETS. GOD, THESE PEOPLE MAKE ME SICK.

And - breathe. It does really annoy me though, everyone around me works and works bloody hard, for the tax man to take our hard earned cash to fund these annoying, lazy bastards! There are some exceptions, I know, but I do know of a few that do it because they can.

Monday 22nd

I bought a pheasant for dinner on Sunday and forgot to write about it. I have never eaten it before and thought it would be a nice treat for me and my boyfriend. I was chewing a piece (I think I cooked it for too long) and crack! I nearly chipped a tooth, I found a bullet in it and my boyfriend said he had never seen anyone have a bullet in it, so I said I would keep it, then two minutes later, crack, he had one!

We decided to throw the bullets away, even though they are meant to be good luck. How they are good luck I'll never understand, it could have been a very expensive trip to the dentist.

Tuesday 23rd

I made a cheesecake for the first time today and my boyfriend did his 'Come Dine With Me' feedback on it. (He would have scored me a ten, I reckon). Anyway later that night he was complaining of a bad tummy , and that it hurt. He said it must have been my cheesecake so he scored me a three. I felt so bad so I made a fuss of him all night, which cheered him up.

Wednesday 24th

Tummy ache, my arse. I am not surprised. I opened the fridge this morning and half the cheesecake was missing. The cheeky git had gone downstairs whilst I was having a soak in the bath and helped himself to extra portions. He owes me big time tonight!

Thursday 25th

I have watched Deal Or No Deal quite a few times lately and it amazes me how greedy people are. They go there with nothing, pick a few boxes, the banker then phones up and offers them forty six thousand pounds, and the prat picking the boxes says in a cocky tone, "Cheers, Mr Banker, but NO deal" and the crowd go wild. I don't know about you, but I have my fingers crossed hoping these greedy people will pick the next three boxes in this order:

1. Two hundred and fifty thousand pounds
2. One hundred thousand pounds
3. Seventy five thousand pounds

Then the crowd go quiet, the banker calls up and offers five thousand pounds. The person picking the boxes hates the offer and again, says all cocky, "No deal." The crowd go wild, then they pick all the high numbers again and end up dealing for about two hundred pounds.

Friday 26th

Cats and Christmas trees do not, I repeat, do *not* get on. I have mislaid six baubles now and probably won't find them until the New Year (when I do my yearly 'new year, new start' clean up). My tinsel is looking strangely like a cat has been tugging and chewing on it, and the stupid animal keeps biting the lights (he won't if he gets a sudden shock).

Sunday 28th

Went sledging today (although hurtling down a steep hill head first on a body board designed for the sea is probably not classed as sledging). I now understand why dads put their kids at the front of the sledges, it is not so we can see more, it is to protect them from the snow spray, we were their snow pillows. It bloody hurts, that snow spraying on your face. Cheers, Dad!

DECEMBER

Wednesday 1st

I wrote my Christmas cards today as it is the first of December, and thought I'd better get started as it usually takes me a few weeks to finish them. I am not writing so many this year, only family and close friends. I am fed up with writing them for work as I always forget somebody and they take offence!

People who update their Facebook status on Christmas Day should be sent to prison! It's like the Twitter thing, I have never understood why people like it or even bother to follow people (it's stalking if you ask me). I really couldn't give a monkeys that someone has just made a cup of tea and the tea bag split, or that they just went to the toilet.

Thursday 2nd

Why on earth do I feel guilty and look as though I have just stolen my car when a police car is following me? Weird!

Friday 3rd

Why does every company help-line offer touch phone help? It is crap, the problem you have is always the last option they give you, by this time you have been on the phone for seven minutes and your bill is already adding up. I got fed up that I couldn't get the answer I wanted from this idiot robot voice, so I called up again and I didn't press anything, and it sent the message thing into a hissy fit and put me straight through to a human. (Bonus. Will do this trick every time now).

Saturday 4th

I am a very happy and proud aunty. It is the first niece or

nephew I have, and it's wonderful, I came over all emotional and the feeling I had going through my body was amazing, it was like all my togs were ticking saying, 'cooeee, you're broody, get practicing', it's so strange how I feel, like I am now pining for something! (Better not tell the boyfriend I do not want to scare him off).

Why is it that when a baby farts on your arm its soooooooo cute, but if your brother or boyfriend farts, generally it is not acceptable?

Monday 6th

Oh dear, I have got the bug for buying cute dresses and things for babies. Oh well, at least I don't feel guilty buying these sorts of clothes. I am not sure my bank would agree, I have spent about the same as I would if the clothes were for me!

Is it just me, or do you wish you could secretly fit into some of these gorgeous baby clothes?

Tuesday 7th

I always feel uncomfortable at the wake of a funeral, because this is when you have the chance to speak to people after the sad funeral service, and what is the first thing I always ask? “Hi, how are you?” or “Are you OK?” What a stupid, stupid question to ask....

Friday 10th

Wanted to make mince pies the other day, so Graham’s son suggested buying the ready-made sweet pastry. Lovely, so when I made them and took them out of the oven, I sprinkled them with icing sugar and they looked and smelt absolutely gorgeous. Oh my God, I took a bite and nearly took my teeth out. I had created concrete pies! Bless, though, my boyfriend still ate one, feeling sorry for me. The worst thing was I offered them to our lodger who eats anything and even he struggled to eat them.

Saturday 11th

Bought puff pastry today, I am supposed to make some mince pies for Christmas Eve for friends and family. I think a trip to the local shop is in order, I'll just sprinkle them with a light dusting of icing sugar, no one will know I didn't make them!

Sunday 12th

It's really strange, my cat goes really weird when a fly is in the house. It doesn't even have to be in the same room as him, but he shakes his head side to side quite quickly like he is going mad, scratches himself and his ears flick frantically, I wonder why that is. I think I am going to have to Google this one. It makes me feel all itchy when he does it.

Monday 13th

So I Google it, apparently it is a method of cat hunting.

Cats will often sway their head from side to side very quickly just before they pounce on their prey. This is important so that when they do pounce that they do not miss their target.

Cats have binocular vision which, when they shake their head quickly, allows them to accurately judge how far away their prey is and so gives them a better chance at hitting their target. I now want to be Cat Woman, that fact is amazing, I can't wait to slip this into a conversation.

Wednesday 15th

My car badly needs cleaning (again). Why does everyone say "I bet you wish you never bought a white car as they are a bugger to keep clean," when you have a white car, but when I had my black car everyone used to say "I bet you wish you didn't buy a black car, they are a bugger to keep clean?" When I had my blue car; well, you get my point, it does not bloody matter what colour car you buy, they are all buggers to keep clean.

Thursday 16th

I woke up at five-thirty a.m. today and was wide awake. The most annoying thing is I made sure I actually turned my alarm off, shame my body clock didn't do the same thing.

Saturday 18th

So I met up with a few of my girls today for a coffee and they were all talking about their Facebook and Twitter gossip. I really felt like a spare part.

I think I may have to start a Twitter account, my reasons being (I know I slated it):

1. Most of my diary inserts are very much like Tweets
2. I don't like Facebook but feel I am missing out on these social sites

3. I want to follow authors to speak to them about their books, as I have a blog, 'minxemoo book review' and people say that Twitter is a good way to network

4. I want to be able to talk about the gossip with my friends

Sunday 19th

Last night my boyfriend suggested that we swapped sides of the bed we sleep on because:

a. I like to read and the lamp is on his side.

b. He also gets up about three times in the night to go to the toilet and the en suite is my side.

c. He always gets hot and my side is nearer the window.

So I thought, *yeah that does make sense*, then he said, "We should swap anyway as you sleep by the door and if anyone breaks in you will cop it first." I should be really chuffed with this comment, but I am not as it has taken him nineteen months to work that out!

Monday 20th

I am reading a really good book at the moment (got to finish mine, come to think of it). It's one of those books that you don't want to put down, but at the same time you don't want to read too much as you don't want it to end!

Tuesday 21st

I bought six boxes of mince pies today for our party, I am going to shove them in the oven five minutes before guests arrive, sprinkle the sides with flour, mincemeat and icing sugar, and maybe a little on me just to add to the illusion of me being in the kitchen baking for hours.

Wednesday 22nd

Just tidied the house. What I can never understand is, I do this properly every couple of months and you always end up with about two black bags of crap! Why do we keep this stuff? I am going to start putting stickers on stuff and see if I throw it out next time....

Thursday 23rd

I put some seeds and bread out in the garden today, (Waitrose, expensive worth-every-penny bakery bread) as I saw on the news that little birds are finding it hard to find food due to the snow. Do you know how the little buggers repay me? They crap all over my clean white bed sheets on the clothes line. I bet it was them damn magpies. I got really annoyed and had a major strop on, Graham said I probably got the birds excited.

Don't you love the fact that mobile phones show you who is calling you, the power of rejecting a call is so lovely. What I don't understand, though, is why people withhold their number. I never answer it because it's either someone you don't like (otherwise they would be in your contacts list), or it's some bloody cold callers wanting to ask a few questions that won't take up too much of your time (my arse, I always get sucked in and end up on there for half an hour).

Monday 27th

We don't have a dishwasher. We have never felt the need for one, but when you have washed up on Christmas Eve entertaining twenty guests, then washing up, then entertaining four people on Christmas Day (four courses) then washing up and then entertaining eight people Boxing Day (three courses) and then washing up, you realise the need for one. Reminder to self; go elsewhere next Christmas, I can't do that again.

Tuesday 28th

Graham has cut his finger quite badly and now he can't wash up and we have to entertain again tonight. By this point I start crying, and wish to God that I get a dishwasher for my next Christmas present. I secretly think he chopped half his finger off just so he doesn't have to wash up, he is so getting a sack of coal next Christmas.

Wednesday 29th

I can't wait until the Christmas sales, Graham has said we can go spending. Oh dear, he never learns! What makes me laugh is you always come home with items of clothing you would never have bought before, it's only because it's in the sales. My wardrobe is full of that sort of crap. Time for a session selling items on eBay, when I can be bothered to take photos, upload them and write some drivel about what a bargain they are. It takes me all day to do all of that for about four items, I might pay my Jack to do it!

Thursday 30th

I have made a decision that next year I am not going to buy any Christmas presents, I am just giving money or vouchers, as it is sickening when you walk into a shop you bought a gift from a few days before and it is now at seventy-five percent off. Seriously, I bought some aftershave for my boyfriend which cost seventy-two pounds (I know, I'm a mug), and by Boxing Day it was reduced down to forty-seven (I know that's not seventy-five percent but it is still a bloody joke).

The problem then was, I was so upset that I had wasted my money and felt done over, I had to do some retail therapy to get over it and spent one hundred and eighty-five pounds doing so.

Friday 31st

I feel so lovely and refreshed today. I slept so well (about fourteen hours) drifting off in a deep sleep, remembering what I bought the other day. Four pairs of gorgeous shoes that I will NOT be able to walk in, and lots and lots of beautiful clothes (some I will never wear). I came home with six bags of stuff! I can't begin to remember every item I purchased, as most was bought on impulse and was a bargain, so I paid for it, bagged it and took it. I will have to check in my purse for the receipts, then I will remember what I bought. My purse is full of crap, I just emptied it and the contents were photos, bank cards, store cards, loyalty cards, receipts, train ticket, newspaper cutting, chewing gum, appointment cards, money, plaster and one headache tablet.

How on earth my purse closed, I will never understand. I think I will have to sort my bag out (might need a black bin liner for the crap hiding in there).

JANUARY

Saturday 1st

Why does alcohol make me think I can sing like Celine Dion? I know for a fact I can't sing, but when I am drunk I just have that urge. We had the family over and some idiot suggested karaoke (the idiot was me), and we had to get into teams. The problem here was that we were in teams of two and we had to share a microphone. Me being a superstar, I made damn sure I had the mic facing me.

Sunday 2nd

I went swimming today and whilst I was getting dressed a mum and her two little Daughters came in, and the mother said to one of them, "I am just off to take your sister to her swimming lesson, DO NOT talk to anyone," and her daughter replied, "but what if I know them?" I had to hold in my laugh. The frantic mother didn't read the safety signs and rushed around by the pool with her shoes on, slipped over and smacked her head on the tiled floor, which knocked her out. The lifeguards came into the changing rooms and asked the little girl what her name was so they could take her to her mum, but the little girl wouldn't speak. I was actually wetting myself laughing behind the fake leather changing room curtain that sticks to you when wet!

Once I finished off my swim, I had a nice hot shower for a change and went to my locker. Oh bugger, I do it every time, towel right at the bottom of the locker under everything so I have to get all my clothes wet. The challenge comes when you're getting dressed (I have worn skinny jeans, shit!), it took me thirty-five minutes to get my clothes back on. Next time I am wearing flip-flops (no more soggy socks), shorts and a loose t-shirt.

Monday 3rd

Why is it that when you book a night or two away you always want a king size bed? But have you noticed that you never use that extra space! We always end up cuddled together in the middle in the spoon position. We always do it and it's about fifty pounds more than a double bed room.

Tuesday 4th

I have started to get fit as my boyfriend is very fit, and I mean super fit, which puts a lot of pressure on me. So I decided to go hill running with him and some of his Fellow followers and I managed one point two miles (they did just over six miles). I feel so great. I ran down the hill and a little way up. Next week I have to do the same, but I have to aim for the tree which is half way back up again, that would make it one point five miles, so here I go. (I think I might train for the Marathon this year).

Wednesday 5th

OMG I can't walk, I can't move my legs or arms. Jesus, I am walking like Whoopi Goldberg. What the hell is happening? It feels like I have been in a serious accident, I am in so much pain. Graham said that this is a good thing. Really? REALLY? He actually runs up and round and down this hill for fun three times.

Even the cars make an uncomfortable noise when they drive up it, my boyfriend is a machine.

Tuesday 11th

Well, I have recovered, although it has taken nearly a week. Went down the hill today and failed on the way up. The tree was so near yet so bloody far, so I just started crying! What I don't understand is that I have never run before and it has never bothered me. Ever! And now I am crying about it? Graham told me it was fine and that this happens. As long as I keep training, I'll be able to run round like they do, "no problem." No problem? I really love that he has such faith in me, the problem is I know I will let him down, so I am going to have to work out how to do it gently.

I have decided that I am going to go on a detox, maybe this will help me to tone up and make me feel fitter!

Thursday 13th

I became a member at the local swimming pool today, and I can't quite let him down yet, so I decided to run there with him (it is under a mile away, so it's OK). I swam twelve lengths and he swam about a hundred and twelve in that time. Now when I go swimming I seem to do this sort of turtleneck breast stroke that makes me look like I am seriously constipated. I really wish I could swim like those people in the fast lanes doing those tumble turns. (Oh look, there goes Graham in the fast lane doing the tumble turns). We then ran home...

Friday 14th

I surprised Graham for his birthday by taking him away (and yes, I booked a room with a king-sized bed). It was the most beautiful romantic place ever, but he had a surprise for me also....we got all our bits and bobs out and hung stuff in the wardrobe and made the massive room (we got an upgrade) and lounge our own,

We decided to have a bit of a birthday treat before going downstairs for a pot of tea and cake, ready for Graham to open his cards and presents. I decided to have a glass of red wine and the glass they came out with was bigger than my face, I knew this was going to be a good weekend.

After Graham was surprised with all his gifts, we went back to our room, had a bath and some more birthday treats (wow, talk about a birthday treat). I had booked our table in the restaurant downstairs for around seven p.m. so we got all dressed up. Graham seemed a little on edge so I asked if he was OK. "Yes I am fine, just tired from the trip here, I think," he answered to me. We had a choice of table so we picked the table tucked away in the corner and put in our wine order and starters. Lovely, lovely starter, couldn't fault it (had rabbit pate served up on a slate). Graham then started to ask me lots of weird questions like, "Gosh, you have drunk a lot of water, do you not need the toilet?"

"No I have not, I have not had one glass of water today!" (Reminds me I must drink more water).

"Are you sure? When did you last go?" I just gave him that look us women are good at (you know, the one that says 'shut up'). He was acting so edgy and not really replying to my questions properly so, I don't know why, I just said, "When are you going to ask me to marry you?" and can you believe it, he was just about to do just that! That explained everything. The silly fool. Of course I said yes, and cried lots and lots and lots. He was trying to get me to go to the toilet so he could get the ring ready and prepare himself! Bless him, I do love him so much, which is a good thing because I have just agreed to marry him! What a perfect weekend this was going to be. A bottle of wine later and phone calls to everyone I know to tell them the news, we went back to our room for some more birthday and engagement treats!

Monday 17th

I have just had my eyelash extensions put on (two bloody hours), apparently I have a lot of eyelashes), my hair extensions put in (well there is nothing like testing out what it will look like for the wedding even though we have not set a date yet and have only just got engaged). The problem I have is, I can't get my eyelashes wet and I need to keep the hair extensions dry, so I will have to give up swimming. I can't possibly wear a swimming hat and goggles. Do you realise how bloody ridiculous it makes you look unless you're some pro! I don't know how to break the news to my fiancé.

Wednesday 19th

I was at my friend Sarah's house and her little boy was talking to his mate (they are only seven by the way), and said, "On the first date, they just tell each other lies, and that usually means they will see each other again." I mean please, really? What sort of things are these kids watching? It's like the other day I phoned to speak to Sarah and he answered, "Hello"

"Wow, you sound out of breath, honey, you OK?" I asked.

"No I don't, I have more breath," he replied. How sweet.

Thursday 20th

Oh my God, I'm never going to lunch with my friend at work (who is way too skinny by the way). We arrived at the restaurant and my friend says, "I'll have the chicken salad, no bacon, no egg, no cheese and no avocado, oh and I want the chicken on a separate plate."

The waitress then replied, "So you just want leaves, olives and tomatoes?"

"Yes," she replied.

"It would be cheaper to get a chicken leg with a side salad."

"NO, I WANT THE CHICKEN SALAD," (she really didn't need to shout, as the whole restaurant was now looking straight at us).

"It would be the same thing, but without all the toppings you don't want." My friend replied rather loudly, and like a four year old shouted, "I WANT CHICKEN SALAD," (Seriously, she needs to pipe down, this is so embarrassing)!

"Ok, what dressing would you like?" replied the waitress patiently.

"I don't want any."

"OK," said the waitress, turning to me. "What would you like to order, madam?"

"Can I have the lamb shanks, mash and carrots. Oh sod it, give me the works!"

When our lunch arrives my friend looks at her plate, then mine, and says, "I wish I ordered what you have got, mine looks really plain and certainly not worth the money."

Friday 21st

Now I don't know about you, I really hate builders that shout stuff to girls, but I did have to laugh today. A very pretty young lady was walking past some builders and one of them shouted, "HELLO?......HELLO?" Within seconds of him saying this, another builder flew out of the Portakabin singing, "Is it me you're looking for"? Fantastic! I love a bit of Lionel Richie.

Sunday 23rd

OK, so I have decided to write a list for the wedding that I need to sort:

1. Dress
2. Shoes
3. Tiara
4. Rings
5. Choose maid of honour
6. Choose bridesmaids
7. Choose venue
8. Choose car
9. Choose invites

My head hurts, I need a break from this, there is so much to think about.

Tuesday 25th

Sarah's son is growing up way too fast. We were listening in on their conversation today and they were talking about some girl at school. We were creasing up but also shocked at the same time, as they are only ten years old. My friend's son says to his mate, "I heard she is a really bad kisser."

"I heard that too, I heard that she tries to eat your face."

"Maybe she was hungry?" Bless them.

Wednesday 26th

God, that silly blonde girl at the office has really embarrassed herself today with her recent speech it was a classic; the whole office just collapsed in laughter. And this is why. "Were you breast fed? Apparently it makes you clever, I wasn't breast fed."

Thursday 27th

I was on the train today and overheard two girls, probably about seventeen, and one of them said to her friend, "If only he didn't go out every night and get shit-faced he would be the perfect boyfriend." I nearly choked on my coffee, was I that thick and naive when I was that age? I will have to ask Sarah, I'm sure we were more clued up than that, mind you I remember one boyfriend I had when I was that age cheating on me, not once, not twice but three times, and I still stayed with him because 'I loved him,' how deluded and young I was!

Saturday 29th

I went into a very expensive shoe shop the other day, I was very excited as I had just got a bonus and felt really posh with this extra money that I could buy a pair of shoes with, without worrying what the bank would say. Found a pair, fell in love, I then saw the price tag (I threw up a little bit in my mouth), two hundred and eighty-seven pounds! Then two muttons dressed as lambs, sorry I mean two rich middle-aged women (who had way too much surgery to look younger) walk in. One turns to the other and says loudly so most of the shop heard, "Oh, I do like the style of those Jimmy Choo shoes." Friend replies, "Oh but, darrrrrrrling, they are too, too similar to those Givenchy shoes you got yesterday." Not that I am bitter or anything, bitches!

Sunday 30th

Andrew was in the kitchen today looking very happy with himself, so I asked him what he was up to and he replied, "Oh I'm on a diet, just got back from the gym, New Year, new start."

"Ooooooh, look at you, Mr, so what are you cooking then?"

"Fish fingers, with veg." *Well done*, I thought, as he didn't really like fish. But when he opened the oven door to get them out he had sixteen, yes sixteen, fish fingers on the tray, and the veg he was referring to was mashed peas covered in tomato ketchup.

FEBRUARY

Tuesday 1st

My friend and I were in town, stood there in a shop queue. The shop assistant said to us, “Sorry about the wait,” my friend then replied, “No need to be sorry, I am happy being this size,” (she is over seventeen stone). I just had to laugh because the poor girl serving didn’t know whether to laugh or to cry.

Now I love my friend dearly and she is really happy being that size, but I just can't understand it. I mean if I went up a dress size, I would think to myself, *better lay off the cakes.* Graham would have me straight down the gym, but if I went up two dress sizes and a couple of stone, I would panic and do something about it. My friend said that she thought that when she piled on four stone, but did sod all about it, and eight stone later she thought, “Oops, I am now a size twenty-two!" But she has stayed that weight and is really truly happy and never without a lover!

Thursday 3rd

I love it when I'm right. Graham wanted a new phone and was banging on about the new Phone 4, and I pointed out to him that this is so different to his Blackberry, which he has always used, and that iPhones are more for the techno geek or youngsters who like apps and Facebook etc. But he was determined and got one anyway. Watch this space!

Saturday 5th

The phone has lasted all of two days, he now wants to take it back and get the new Blackberry instead. I couldn't stop laughing and asked him why, and he said, "I don't understand it, and I keep muting people because of the touch screen." I want him to get the Blackberry anyway, because they throw in a forty-inch TV with it!

Monday 7th

Why do we slam the phone down like it's the phone's fault, when the person on the other end of it annoyed you? I better be careful soon, as I'm getting a touch screen phone and don't want to shatter the bloody phone (I don't have insurance).

Wednesday 9th

I have been talking to a few new brides to get some advice from them. Apparently you need to book a venue at least twelve months before the wedding to get what you want. We have decided to get married this September, so that leaves me only seven or eight months! Must make a list of ideas: hotel, barn, castle, manor house, boat, golf club, football club, pub, leisure centre (last case scenario)

Thurdsay 10th

I can't get over how bad I am at those games for my

Nintendo ds. They state on the game that it's for age seven plus, yet I can't complete them without going onto the internet to get the cheats for the games. Sarah's son thinks I am sad and thick that I have to do this, and he completed the same game I am on in five days. I am on the fourth level and it has taken me two weeks to get that far!

Saturday 12th

I went running today as it was wild outside, raining really hard. Everyone driving past avoided the puddles that would have drowned me in the sewage rain water, but this one dick of a taxi driver decided it would be funny to drive through it and cover me. My mum would have gone mad if she heard what I called him! I hope that someone throws up in his taxi at the weekend, in fact it looks rather like the taxi I threw up in a few months back!

Monday 14th

I got a lovely text from one of my best friends today; '*A women should have one friend who makes her laugh and one who lets her cry.*' I must text my girls and tell them how much they mean to me and that we need to meet up, it's been too long.

Lovely text from Graham; '*What's for dinner?*'

Tuesday 15th

My friend at work told me that her boyfriend and she had been out for a meal at the weekend, and when they were walking to their car a homeless man asked them if they had any spare change, and her boyfriend replied, "No mate, but I have a fag you can have."

"Yes please, cheers, mate."

So her boyfriend got out his pack of fags and before he got one out the homeless guy said, "Oh, don't worry about it, I don't smoke them, they taste horrible." What a fussy tramp!

Friday 18th

Oh dear, spent half the morning at work calling up venues. The hotel wanted thirty two thousand for a hundred guests to have a sit down meal and disco. I nearly had a panic attack on the phone and made out I lost the signal and hung up. As for the castle, I didn't even have the balls to call them, I did a recce online and only the rich and famous could afford it.

The golf club was reasonable but I didn't like the set up they had, it only held sixty people and in that sixty I had to include the DJ's and waiters!

The football club was cheap, and I knew why when they gave me their website address, I would rather get married in my local public toilets.

The barn was lovely, and well in our budget, and so was the boat. I now have a dilemma. Bridezilla, here I come.

Saturday 19th

I don’t know where I got to about writing about the house, but for now we are staying put! We have decided the B&B idea is a no go area at the moment, but we still keep looking at houses in Wales just in case! I am focused on the wedding so much, to the point where I turn my computer on for work and just end up looking through my emails to see if I have had any replies from my caterers, dressmakers, wedding ring suppliers or any other wedding updates. It's slowly taking over my life! I have already been doodling my new signature (it took me years to perfect my current one). I have even changed my normal magazines to bridal ones, the problem with those are they are more expensive, but you do get free gifts with them. This month I got a free wedding napkin! At least they only come out monthly, so I can justify the cost. I have realised already that last month's is identical to the previous months, apart from the front cover, but I had to get it as it had a free L-plate with it for your hen do. (Even though I said I would never wear one).

Sunday 20th

You need to get a loan out these days to go out to the cinema, it cost my fiancé and me seventeen pounds to see a film and two pounds eighty for a bag of sweets (I can get these sweets two for one pound at our local). Oh, and three pounds seventy for a coffee. I remember when you could go out with ten pounds and have change.

I must be getting old, I can't believe I just wrote that. I remember when my parents said about the half penny and pound notes, and how I laughed at them; well the other day I showed my fiancé's son an old fifty pence, ten pence and five pence and how he laughed and said I was old!

(Thanks, I'm not even thirty yet!)

Monday 21st

Why do we shout on our mobile phones when the other person is quiet? For example, today I called a customer and he was in an area of bad reception, so I shouted so he could hear me better, which wouldn't have helped at all, I just got that look off everyone in the office to say, shut it!

Thursday 24th

I was reading some of my friends Facebook friends' statuses today (as I do not have a Facebook page because I hate it), and some really made me laugh.

"I know the world isn't going to end in 2012 because my yoghurt expires in 2013."

"I like to name my iPod 'Titanic' so when it says 'syncing Titanic' I click 'cancel' and feel like a hero."

"If Barbie is so popular, why do you have to buy her friends?"

"I remember when apple and blackberry used to be fruits."

"Poke me if you're horny."

"Am I a perv for touching my door's knob all day?"

Friday 25th

I can't believe it, they say you learn something new every day. Well I have learnt six new things today:

1. The first product to have a bar code was Wrigley's gum. Someone told me this at work after they found they had some stuck to their trousers.

2. It takes seven seconds to get food from your mouth to your stomach. This worries me because I don't go to the toilet (number two) very much so I must have a load still inside me.

3. There are, on average, one hundred and eighty sesame seeds on a bun of a Big Mac (this was told to me by

someone at work scoffing down a MacDonald's whilst I was eating my salad) and who the hell has the time to count all these seeds? Probably the non-workers who shouldn't be claiming benefits.

4. More than ten people a year are killed by a vending machine falling on them. This was said to me at work when I punched the vending machine after my crisps got stuck.

5. The first owner of the Marlboro company died of lung cancer. This was overheard by me when someone was in front of me in the queue buying a packet of cigarettes.

6. Women mature much faster than men. I didn't just learn this but I had to write it because it's so true.

Monday 28th

I don't dislike many people, but there is this one guy at work who types with one finger and it bloody irritates the hell out of me.

MARCH

Wednesday 9th

I have a few days off from work so I went round to clean our other property today, as it's nearly ready to go onto the market. The boys sent me to B&Q with a list of bits to get! I was in there for over an hour to find six items. The reason it took so long was:

1. They wrote 'need screws for sockets, two inch' but didn't write how many.

2. They needed about five bulbs for the kitchen but no size or wattage.

3. They needed white paint, but not what sort; matt, silk or gloss?

Us women would not give a list to our men, send them down town and say, I need a pair of brown jeans, a white blouse and a pair of boots, and not give them the full description, size, material and exact colours, (in fact you would NEVER send them down there).

Monday 14th

I was following a lorry to work on the M25. It was a Primark lorry which should have stated on the side, '*Primark, look good*,' but this lorry was so dirty somebody had crossed out the 'good' and put 'shit', so it read, '*Primark, look shit.*' I laughed so much I nearly crashed. About five minutes later I actually stopped laughing, as I realized that half of what I was wearing was from Primark! I knew then my day couldn't get any worse.

Friday 18th

I have chosen my best friend to be my maid of honor. She is beside herself, and I'm now worried because she has made it very clear that lots of men, booze, music and food will be involved!

Wednesday 23rd

When I went to one of the offices in London I went over to use the fax machine as I had lots of paperwork to fax over to someone, but this machine takes forever, and I mean forever. When I started using it, some bright spark shouted over,“Errrr, I was using that.” I replied, “Errrr, no you were not. Nobody was.” Why do people insist on telling blatant lies? This bloke is a tit, though. He says things like, “There ain't no cups left to have a cuppa in, best get the women in there pronto to wash 'em up, in fact they can bloody well make the brew an' all.” And he wonders why he is divorced!

Saturday 26th

Do you think there is rubbish on the TV these days? I have had a couple of days off from work and the TV has been on in the background, I don’t know why, as it annoys the hell out of me. I have come up with some new headlines for these shows…

1. I am a so-called celebrity, punch my face in

2. My nan left me a crystal vase, how much is it worth?

3. Shit in the attic

4. Waste of time roadshow

Wednesday 30th

Technology and parents… My mum, bless her, gets an email, then prints the email, reads the printed email, hand-writes a reply, and then gives it to dad, who then types and sends her reply!

APRIL

Sunday 3rd

OK, so it's Mother's May. I am not a mother yet, but my Graham has a son, so I am nearly a step-mum. I took my 'nearly stepson' to town to get his mother something, so I thought it was only fair that I bought myself something. I ended up buying a pair of new shoes, a jumper, a shirt and some make-up.

Tuesday 5th

I have done a few car boots lately, as we are moving to my parents' for a few weeks before we move to our little house to start the developing (this is something we really need to get done, Graham has always wanted to do this). A few things I have noticed since I have started car booting:

1. Why do people who pick up a board game or puzzle you are selling ask if all the pieces are there? As if you would tell them if they were not!
2. You're selling a designer dress/top and they ask how much. You reply, "Four pounds for that," then they put it back. I mean, for goodness sake, it cost me eighty pounds and I have worn it twice, I can assure you, you would not get it any cheaper in a charity shop.
3. I always get smelly weird men or ladies who end up staying near me and talking to me about crap. You don't want to be rude, so you feel you have to talk to them about crap!
4. When you're queuing to get into the car boot, people (usually shifty looking men) knock on your window and ask, "Any rings, watches, Mobile phones?" (Even if I did, I wouldn't sell it to them).

5. It's really scary when you pull up at your pitch and men hear the sound of screws and hammers being placed on the floor, they flock around you and dive in. I made about one hundred pounds selling that crap to those men. (I am going to ask all my friends' dads if I can raid their garages. This stuff is like gold!

Friday 8th

Been to the tip today, and I said to our lodger that if he had anything that needs taking, to leave it by the front door. Well, one of his bags was filled with pornos. How did I know this? Well, the bag was full of them and had a tear in the bag, and a breast was staring at me! Anyway, I scooped up the bags and threw them into the skip and sped off again, hopefully unnoticed.

When I got home there was another load to take, so off I went back down there. I left it a good hour so they may have had a shift change at the tip. I changed my top as a disguise, then when I pulled up they all started smirking at me. I was so embarrassed they must have thought I was a right old slapper, or that I had just found my partner's stash and threw them out in an argument.

Monday 11th

I finished work early today, and I was lying in the sun thinking of jobs that I could do that meant I didn't have to wait for the weekends for time off, so here are the ideas I have come up with:

1. Dog walking – PROBLEM; I don't like dogs mess and I am not a great fan of dogs either.
2. Cleaning houses – PROBLEM; I can just about do mine.
3. Do car boots full time – PROBLEM; my last few experiences have put me off for life.

4. Be an ice cream woman – PROBLEM; it's never sunny and I would probably eat all the profit!

5. Become a mum – PROBLEM; need to convince Graham (this is my favorite one though, as I would love to be a mummy).

Tuesday 12th

I feel so embarrassed. I went into Tesco to buy my friend a necklace set, and I went up to a women (who was wearing a blue suit standing next to the shelf stacking equipment) and asked where I could find these. She replied in a rather pissed off voice, "How the hell would I know, does it look like I work here?" I did feel like saying, "Well yes, that's why I asked you," but I thought I'd better not as she probably would have punched me and she looked a hard-faced cow.

Wednesday 13th

All I do is moan.

Thursday 14th

A colleague just got back from holiday and the first thing they said was, "A six week holiday makes you realise how much you actually hate your job." I was a bit shocked by this statement as, it takes me about two days to realise that!

Saturday 16th

We have been having some rather warm weather lately, so the first hot day I was out in the garden sun bathing in my bikini, no sun cream, lush! Give me a tan, baby!

Sunday 17th

I had a bath this morning and got stuck to it, I look like a bloody lobster, why didn't I just put some sun lotion on yesterday? I am so sore, my fiancé keeps laughing at me saying, "I told you so," but I am putting on a brave face pretending it doesn't hurt, I am actually melting, I can feel it.

Tuesday 19th

Bongo is so clever, he goes out and then worries the hell out of us, as he disappears for ages and never comes in when he is called by his name. But as soon as you shout "TREATS," he comes bolting over the fence and straight to his treats cupboard. Genius! He probably sits behind the fence mocking us at how gullible we are, falling for his 'I have gone missing' trick!

Thursday 21st

Been looking at the bed and breakfast idea again in Wales! I think this is something we really will do.

May

Sunday 1st

My friends think it's strange that I go to the pitch and putt with my other half and just sit in the car! Now I am writing this, it does seem a little odd! It's great, though, I get to read whilst hearing nothing but birds tweeting. I have just realized that there are two other women doing exactly what I am doing.

I wonder how many women do this too, and where else they go with their other half to just sit in the car to read.

Friday 6th

I went running on my own today. I thought, as my other half wasn't with me, I could walk and run, but every time I was about to stop and walk someone appeared so I had to carry on so they didn't think I was a crap runner, (which I am by the way, I look like I am having a fit, not keeping fit). I have never ran so far, why can't these people stop appearing and piss off. I need to walk, I am knackered!

Monday 9th

We have moved back to my parents' for a couple of weeks just whilst our house is ready. Where do I start?

We moved in five days ago and the television is now not working properly, our cat wakes them up at five in the morning, we have got through six rolls of loo roll, I don't know how, and now the loo is blocked!

Bang goes my inheritance. God knows what they tell their friends, I bet they are counting down the days till we leave now

.

Friday 13th

I don't think I can ever eat another sweet potato. My brother's wife was changing my niece's nappy and said'

"Oh what a hot, squelchy soft poo'" just as I was biting into my hot, squelchy soft potato.

Monday 16th

I HATE WORK. FACT.

Tuesday 17th

We have decided on a car we want for the wedding (well, what I want, anyway). I have just put a deposit down on a top of the range E Class Mercedes with a chauffeur in a flat cap and tux! I would have gone with horses and carriage, but I am scared of horses, for one, and it is going to be at least twenty miles away from the two venues we are yet to decide on.

Thursday 19th

I HATE CUSTOMERS. FACT.

Monday 23rd

We have booked the bloody venue, I can't believe it! We did have to change the date to the following week, though, due to some other people wanting to marry there, how dare they! We are to marry on HMS Warrior in Portsmouth. I am glad we are not having the horses, as it is forty miles away from home! We have a viewing around the ship next week!

Wednesday 25th

I HATE THE M25. FACT.

Tuesday 30th

I am on such a high at the moment. Getting married is so easy, why do people make out it's so stressful to organise? Stressful is sitting in a traffic jam on the motorway. Stressful is having a customer moaning that something is wrong, and demanding you sort it even though it has nothing to do with you. Stressful is getting an unexpected phone bill through the post for a hundred and forty pounds! I am so happy to be organising mine, I am getting to use some of my stationery doing so (everything is colour coordinated)!

JUNE

Wednesday 1st

I HATE THE WEATHER. FACT.

Saturday 4th

I went into a charity shop today to buy some more books to read (I seriously could open my own library now), and a lady was in front of me and said to the worker, "Excuse me dear, I really like this top, do you have it in a size sixteen?"

"This is a charity shop," the worker replied.

"Yes, that's very nice, dear, but I need a sixteen, have you got this in a size sixteen?" the lady replied.

"No, this is a charity shop. People donate their clothes so what comes in, we sell," replied the worker.

"Well that's no good is it, you wouldn't get Marks and Spencer doing that. How stupid, no wonder it's not very busy in here," replied the lady and walked off. With that, me and the worker just burst into laughter and could not believe what just happened.

Sunday 5th

Oh no, the hot water and heating has just packed up at my parents' house. Dad's not happy!

Monday 6th

I went into a supermarket today to grab some lunch and thought I would use those self-service machines to save time. Well, what can I say? The red light kept coming on as it did not recognize the weight of some items once scanned then put in the bagging area. The machine is so rude, it shouts at you! Some things are too light so it states you are about to steal something (as good as anyway). It never takes your notes unless they are brand new and not creased, so I argue with the machine and tell it there is no such thing as a crisp note anymore! Whilst you are putting your change away, it shouts at you to take your receipt and to remove your bags! The bloody cheek.

But the funniest thing was when a stupid man was making all these loud tutting noises and swearing at the machine, so the lady came over to assist asking, “Is everything OK, sir?”

“No it's not, I am trying to get a price for my spuds but I can’t find them on the bloody category list, it's bloody useless.”

“What are you typing in to find your s*puds,* sir?”

With that he realized what he had done, went red and proceeded to type ‘potatoes' (not spuds) and the bloody category list bloody found them.

Wednesday 8th

Do you know what really bugs me? When you lend a pen to somebody and they chew it, it's bloody disgusting. I am going to start rubbing my pens round the rim of a toilet before I loan them to people.

Monday 13th

Stuck on the M25 again this morning and listened to the weather as it's been really hot but looked rather misty today. It was a classic; 'mostly cloudy, some mist around, scattered showers, heavy in places. The roads will be dry unless it raining.' OK, so how do I become a weather reader, as I know they are paid a lot and they just sit there making the weather up. Even I could do that! Today the weather may be sunny with a slight shower or maybe snow, the roads will be dry but may become wet if rain and skiddy if snow settles, that is if we get some.

Tuesday 14th

My local Chinese fish and chip shop have a pot-bellied Buddha that sits on the counter and it really looks like some of the people I know. Anyway, some drunk louts came into the shop and pushed their way to the front of the queue. An old boy piped up and said, "Oi, there is a queue you know;" with that, the fattest member of this smelly gang stated, "I am a preferred customer, look they even have a statue of me in here." I did have to laugh because it did look like him. With that the old boy, who really needs to learn to shut up otherwise he may just get a good kicking, said, "We were here first, and anyway, we need to order before you as there won't be anything left after you put your order in."

It was a very awkward six minutes wait for my food.

Thursday 16th

Whenever one of the managers at work puts adverts in the

paper for a new job role, he puts 'reply in person'. Now I am thinking he does this so he can tell you to bugger off if you're too old, fat or ugly, and his way of telling them 'no' is to say the position has been filled. The sales teams look like the cast of Baywatch.

Friday 17th

I was bored at work today, so I amused myself (which is very childish) by changing all the settings on the photocopying machine. I have never heard so many swear words being used in our office. It was so funny, everyone blaming each other. Someone actually phoned the photocopying company up to complain it was not working.

Sunday 19th

WOW! The ship is amazing, although the stairs down to the toilets are a bit steep, God help some of my relatives.

It was so strange going on board. I remember going on a school trip twenty three years ago, getting home telling my mum that one day I was going to be a princess and live on a boat just like this, where the hell has that time gone?
I can now live that dream for a day, become a princess and marry my prince and live that day to the max.

Friday 24th
We went to Isle of Wight for a camping trip to check out the area, as this is one of the places we could set up a bed and breakfast. We stayed in Sandown, such a beautiful place. We arrived Saturday morning and visited every part of the island by seven o'clock that night!
I must say the daytime is so wonderful, you feel a million miles away from anywhere. Added bonus is, there is not one motorway, But at night, oh dear God, where the hell did all these strange people appear from? It was awful - the youths were hanging around drinking and smoking,

looking at you as though you are their next victim. (This was not in Sandown, I must add).

We did meet a couple of people on our trip and learnt a few facts which did impress me. There are twenty one tourists to every one resident on the island, with approximately one hundred and forty thousand residents on the island. The island has more sunshine than any other UK resort. (I do believe this as it was bloody lovely when we were there and back home was just overcast).

Apparently in 1988 a cat-like dinosaur 'yet to be named' was discovered, twelve feet long, with murderous claws, razor-sharp teeth and long hind legs! I didn't sleep well that night, because every damn noise I heard outside I was convinced it was the dinosaur cat!

Sunday 26th

Why is it when you buy your tent it's all neatly packed away in the extra small bag it came in, but when it's time to pack up and leave, it takes you about six attempts to make it fit? In the end you just put the tent in the bag and use an extra bag for the ground sheet and pegs. I can't be the only one who always has this problem! I just know, the next time we go camping, we will have to go out and buy new pegs or a new ground sheet as we will have lost these ones.

Monday 27th

Had a phone call today from a mobile phone company and they asked me when my phone expires, so I said "August 2012", over sixteen months away. He then asked "Are you looking to renew a contract anytime soon?" I said, "No I have sixteen months left of my existing one;" he then said, "OK, do you want to buy one for a family member?" I put the phone down.

JULY

Saturday 2nd

I hate cold callers, how do they get hold of your number and details? Within days of owning a new phone and number, they call you!

Sunday 3rd

We're not going to move to the Isle of Wight now.

Monday 4th

I was in town today waiting for the bank to open, I swear they open later every day. Across the road there was a MacDonalds, with a little snotty child stood outside whining to his mum, "I want to go to MacDonalds now, I want to go, I want a MacDonalds, I want one, I want one." Mother replies, "No". "I WANT A MACDONALDS,"

shouts the snotty little shit, and with that threw himself on the floor. The mother replied, “If you don’t get up and shut up, you'll be getting a SMACK DONALDS.”
Child got up. I and a few others chuckled to ourselves, I must remember that one.

Tuesday 5th
I was following a car home from work today for ages and noticed a sticker on the back that read, ‘*I haven’t spoken to my wife for twelve months, I don’t like to interrupt her.*’
When I got to overtake and saw the driver, the sticker should have stated, *I haven’t spoken to my wife for twelve months because I look like a miserable sod*!’
There are so many sour faced people around at the moment. Why can’t people just be happy they are alive, we only have one chance in life! My granddad used to say you live every day, you only die once!

Wednesday 6th

Got a quote back from a company who makes wedding invites today, seven hundred and seventy-five pounds for sixty invites! I deleted that email and have decided to pay my friend to make them. All I have to do is buy the stuff and she will make them for sixty pounds (fingers crossed they look like I paid seven hundred and seventy-five pounds for them)!

Saturday 9th

Went round to Sarah's house this morning and she told me her little girl was packing her bag with a pretend cake, a Peppa pig book, toy car keys and a dolly. My friend asked her what she was doing, her reply was, "Going to work" as though that was a normal thing a two year old does. Then she asked her, "Where"? and she replied "Jane's, I am going to Jane's work." Basically, every time I see her when I am dropping something off, I always say, "Anyway, better get off, I have got to go to work!"

Sunday 10th

Why do we feel fine walking around in our bikinis but would never dream of walking around in our bra and knickers?

Wednesday 13th

I work around London a lot and whilst waiting to see a customer, a banker (I assume) walked out of one of the well-known banks on his phone and said, "The figures just don't add up Stu, I'm worried." Now the thought going through my mind was, if they can't add it up and work it out, then we are all bloody screwed, AGAIN!

Friday 15th

Today I saw the best sign in a shop window CLOSED DUE TO ILLNESS. It was a health shop!

Monday 18th

Today I found out that every time you lick a stamp you consume one tenth of a calorie! This now explains why the cashiers in post offices are larger than most cashiers! I wonder if they could complain, and use the human rights card to sue them for making them overweight? In fact, that's why I probably put a few pounds on over the Christmas period, sending all those cards!

Tuesday 19th

I have just read that FACT, if you bang your head against a brick wall it uses one hundred and fifty calories an hour. Why on earth would anyone try that and actually think of it to try out and then write about this STUPID fact! Surely scientists should be finding cures for cancers and diseases, not losing weight by banging your head against a brick wall?

Wednesday 20th

Wow, my friend has done a tester invite and I am well impressed! I have given her the go-ahead. What a bloody saving! I think she wants to be a bridesmaid. We have decided on a page-boy and one bridesmaid so far, I am so excited, it's creeping up on us fast.

Thursday 21st

I am fed up with my figure and wanted to start exercising again but I really can't be arsed, so I tried banging my head against the wall. I got to twenty six times, I still look the same but with a raging headache so had to buy some head ache tablets, which cost me two pounds eighty-eight, (could have bought two hundred and eighty eight bags at

WH Smiths for this) and a nice lump on the side of my head.

Note to self, do not bang head against any wall, ever!

Monday 25th

Lost my diary the other day, only just found it. I left it at work on my desk. I hope no-one has read it! I would read it if I found a diary, I love knowing what people have been up to!

AUGUST

Tuesday 2nd

Holy shit, what a hen weekend to remember! I was blindfolded all the way to Brighton (not good when you get travel sick). Arrived at a wonderful spa hotel. I thought my maid of honour had done good, I couldn't wait for a relaxing weekend.

Relaxing is certainly not the word, I got in the shower and when I got out all twenty hens (mum, nan, aunties, cousins, friends, in-laws-to be) were standing in my room wearing hula hula girl outfits! I knew then that my maid of honour had made a massive error, and I can still swipe her of her maid of honour role and make her just a guest.

My mother and sister-in-law to be had decided to get the shots flowing early to prepare us for the evening ahead. They had booked a night club VIP area, all the hens couldn't wait as we had pant-less waiters, oh dear God. (This made me throw up a little in my mouth).

I have never seen or ever want to see my nan dancing like she did with that man, ever ever again in my life. I didn't know she could bend like that. I had just got into the groove and was dancing away, when some of the hens dragged me back to the VIP area and shouted, "IS THERE A FIRE IN HERE? IT'S KIND OF HOT." Oh dear God, a horrid, steroid, oily pin-headed fireman stripper arrived and started to gyrate against me.

Now I am up for a laugh, but this is my worst fucking nightmare. He stripped to his thong (I HATE MEN IN THONGS), covering me in cream and then himself, trying to get me to lick it off. He stank of B.O and there is no way on this earth I was licking a stranger who has probably been licked ten minutes before by another poor hen, so I said, "No thanks! But I am sure a few of the hens wouldn't mind having a go!" Jesus, I have never seen anything like it. My family and friends were like a pack of wolves. The poor fireman looked so scared, he actually called for help and my aunty and a few others got pulled off and warned by the bouncers!

After that, all my hens got wasted (so did I). Next minute, the lights came on and it was three a.m. We all looked like we had been in a car pile-up. Make-up everywhere, covered in oil and cream, sweat, drink. One of my hens had sick on her as well, classy.

Got a kebab on the way back to the hotel, I have never actually eaten one sober, but when you're pissed, it's heaven in a wrap. The next day, oh dear God, woke up and my tongue felt like carpet and I swear I had been kicked in the head! I went to my room alone, but had woken up with two other hens in my room, when did they arrive? We had massages and a treatment each booked the morning after. After having my massage I had to stop half way through, as I needed to throw up! Why do I drink?

Wednesday 3rd

Found out why I had two hens in my room, they had a major leak in their bathroom so they had to share with one of us, and I had the biggest room and was the only one who didn't refuse to let them share my room (in my defence, I was out cold). When we checked out, they took off a hundred pounds off the total bill and gave us all a free half day spa ticket each!

Friday 5th

Today I found out that 111,111,111 x 111,111,111= 12,345,678,987,654,321.... God, I need to get out more.

Sunday 7th

A very close friend of mine has become pregnant, and she was trying to explain to her youngest daughter that she was going to have a new brother or sister (this was explained to her as she wondered why mum's tummy was getting bigger).

My friend said, "Now in a few months' time, mummy will be having a baby so you will have a little brother or sister to play with. You can feel mummy's tummy if you like, as the baby is in here." Her little girl walked off, satisfied with this answer, then about ten minutes later she asked, "Do you have a baby in your bum too?" I tried not to laugh as I could see my friend was so upset!

Wednesday 10th

I had a pub lunch with a workmate of mine today, I went up to the bar to order our food when an old boy came in and the barman asked, "Usual?"

"Good God, man no, I'm driving, I'll just have a pint of Guinness followed with just the one whiskey!"

I couldn't believe it, it's nice to see that everyone follows the drink driving law.

Friday 12th

OK, so today I have nearly been in three fatal accidents! I know this seems a lot in one day but I can honestly say that they were not my fault. They all involved old people. One couldn't see over the steering wheel and looked like her eyes were closed and decided that a red light meant 'GO'. The second one was an old boy in a Porsche, what the hell does someone at the age of eighty need a car like that for? He was in the fast lane on the dual carriageway, going forty five mph so the person behind flashed him to move over, but the old boy ignored him. So the man behind decided to undertake, which is silly of him really and it's illegal, but when he did this the old boy decided to go into the slow lane, causing the other guy to slam his brakes on and throw himself back in my lane and nearly kill me. The third was an old women stopping suddenly to turn left. Instead of slowing down, I nearly went up the back of her,

I would like to point out that she was not indicating either. I think that the government should bring in a law once you hit seventy you must retake your driving test, and everyone MUST have an eye test.

Sunday 14th

I am still struggling with writing my book. I have read about eighteen books in the last few months (all sorts of books) to try and give me ideas, but it's bloody useless, I seriously have got writers block, I used to take the piss when someone said that.

Monday 15th

OH MY GOD, I am soooooooooooooooooooooooo BORED! I have just spent three hours in the most boring meeting ever on this planet.

I had this meeting with a bunch of toffs talking absolute bollocks about two different types on consistency of the same product. I DONT GIVE A TOSS (if I was a celebrity, 'get me out of here'). I just smiled sweetly and pretended I knew what they were all on about. I even started to laugh like I have never laughed before and started saying things like, "Yar, Yar," and "I agree". WTF..... why do I do it? I always feel I have to be like the person I am with and not myself when I am in a meeting, it's scary. I need a new job, either that or go insane!

I have decided to stop writing my diary until after the wedding, as it is all getting too much, I know I said it was easy but I was horrible mistaken, it's a fucking headache!

MR AND MRS

OK, so the wedding. I haven't really mentioned much about it really as I was going to leave it out, as I have a wedding journal and couldn't be arsed to write in both, but decided it would be nice to write it in my diary so in years to come my children can amuse themselves!

So here goes, this is my journal.

The morning of the wedding, OH MY GOD! I was awake by four a.m., I just couldn't sleep so I texted everybody I had on my phone, and amazingly four people replied, what the hell were they doing up? Anyway we were not getting married until five-fifteen p.m. so that's like, let's see, thirteen hours away!!

I have been sick nearly three times already, so I had a 'calm me down' rose wine at about eleven a.m! Shortly after my wine I got a text from my maid of honour saying

'Just seen your future husband in town'.' How is he?' I asked. She replied, *'Cool as really, he is about to have breakfast with his mates, then he is going to chill for a-bit'.*

CHILL A BIT! Does he not know what the BLOODY HELL I am going through?

I really want to text him, but we promised each other no contact from yesterday morning until we meet at the wedding!

I have been sitting up thinking about all the hard work that has gone into ordering everything from the clothes, to the band, to the venue! I still think I am mad, agreeing to my future husband that we will not know what each other will be wearing. I hope to God he does not turn up in fancy dress!

Day 1 as Mr and Mrs

OMG, my head really hurts. We have got to start driving soon to our honeymoon destination! After our night of passion, well I think it was full of passion, my husband would probably say it was more wild due to me being quite drunk. I felt so sexy but, again, my husband would probably say I looked drunk and was not as attractive! The wedding was so fantastic, it really was. So many happy memories will be stored in my brain forever, although some of the memories are a tad blurry! We had a lovely breakfast cooked by my mum at their house, *our mum and dad's*. I'm going to love saying this 'ours'. Balloons were tied to the car and off we went. CLANK CLANK CLUNCK CLUNCK BOOM HISS CLANK CLANK. That's the noise coming from the car thirty miles into the journey. We pulled over, my husband (love it) got out and gave it the once over (by kicking the wheels and moving the luggage around). Fixed, he said. CLANK CLANK

CLUNK CLUNK. On our way back to our mum and dad's to pick up the other car! First test to our marriage.
So we finally arrive at the town (a sleepy town). Oh my God, there were people everywhere, they must have known the new Mr and Mrs was arriving. We found out it was the annual firework weekend display! It was romantic though, watching the fireworks from the bathroom (bath was massive). We had our dinner in the beautiful dining room and another couple came in and sat near us. Talk about opposites attract, she was a vegetarian (she ordered everything vegetarian) and he ordered rare steak and rabbit pate.

Day 2 as Mr and Mrs

Have you ever had snails? Eyeballs covered in snot, is all I can say. Woke up next morning feeling very queasy and very sleepy, I'm putting that down to the snails.

Day 3 as Mr and Mrs

Just woke up and my husband was lying next to me.

Day 4 as Mr and Mrs

My husband decided to take me for a walk called 'lovers walk'. So excited, so I put on my tweed suit and my new wedges (designer wedges), I started to get worried when we got halfway through the walk and it stated 'cliff edges', I was so scared, and a few heavy duty walkers gave me 'the stupid girl' look. Shoes ruined – CHECK, Blisters (lots of) – CHECK, Feet sore – CHECK, Feeling sick - CHECK. Second test to our marriage.

Day 5 as Mr and Mrs

I ate lamb's neck and lamb's glands this evening.

Day 6 as Mr and Mrs

I feel sick, why didn't they put on the menu 'lamb's neck

and glands'? All it said was 'melody of lamb'!

I feel really strange today, and awful for my husband because I seem to be so tired and feel really sick at the moment. I don't want to ruin the honeymoon.

Day 7 as Mr and Mrs

Woken up at two thirty in the bloody morning by some local drunks, then again at five thirty by the bloody dustman, and by seven in the morning we were awake and up and ready to get the hell out of this place. Looking out the window is like the M25 with all the lorries and traffic (lazy town, my arse). We have come away to relax and have lazy mornings. Third test to our marriage.

Day 8 as Mr and Mrs

Got lost today, the next destination should have taken four hours but it had taken seven hours. He blamed my map-reading skills. Sorry, I forgot I was born with a sat nav in my head. Forth test to our marriage

Day 9 as Mr and Mrs

Arrived at Edinburgh, I love it, love it, love it! I want to move here, it's so stunning, we went shopping and I found a ten pound note on the floor. Bonus!

We bought some lovely things, my husband bought some real lamb's wool socks (I wonder if it was from the lambs we ate the other night, I feel sick thinking about it).

The hotel is beautiful. We went straight to the spa, had a sauna, but I had to leave that as I was not feeling to great so I went to our room for a snooze. The hotel cost over two hundred pounds per night, so when we arrived the place looked stunning from the outside and the lobby, wow! When the porter showed us to our room I was a little upset as we went into the lift, leaving a stunning corridor then ping, door opens onto this concrete car park-looking corridor, and showed us to our room which had only our room and one other (probably the broom cupboard). The stairs next to our room leads to doors that the bins get taken to, down a grotty stinking alley way).

Day 10 as Mr and Mrs

I tried haggis and potato scones this morning (not bad), had to stuff my face ready for our next road trip (Saint Andrews). My husband was in his element, I really can't see the fuss myself, it's just a golf course. He looked so happy, smacking the balls at the driving range, I had to take photos of him everywhere. There are more photos of him and that golf course than me and him together!

It is strange the rules here, as back home you are not allowed on the golf course unless you have golf shoes and smart trousers and top, but out here any one can come and play. We were eating lunch and I turned to look out the window, and there was a family of five wearing what looked like clowns outfits. There was even a man on a mobility scooter (felt sorry for the professional lot stuck behind them).

Day 11 as Mr and Mrs

When my husband said we were off to Perth next, I almost wet myself with excitement that we were off to Australia, He then kindly explained to me it is in fact in Scotland! I won't be wearing my bikini then, I worked bloody hard to get this figure!

Day 12 as Mr and Mrs

Went to the top of the Cairngorms Mountain Range. Oh my God, it's too high, I had to pull over as I felt sick and couldn't drive, so we swapped seats. My husband has a death wish I am sure, (we have no life insurance yet), he keeps bloody hanging off things and getting close to cliff edges to take photos. We later drove on and went to a light house and we saw seals. I couldn't stop laughing because we saw a 'shag' diving in and out of the water, I didn't believe my husband when he told me what it was called. I need to grow up.

Day 13 as Mr and Mrs

Next stay was at a farm house, it looked OK from the outside although it had a strange extension, how they got planning permission I will never know. We were showed to our room and all I can say is, DANGEROUS! They had a low beam going straight across the walkway from the door to the bed, my husband has walked into it three times already and we have only been here forty minutes.

When we went to bed (which was about seven in the evening, we were both knackered), we thought we would have a bit of fun, but that quickly fizzled out as a family of four turned up and were shown to their room which was attached to ours, and we could hear every word. So as newlyweds, the night of passion was a no no. We were scared to hold each other's hand just in case they heard us. Eventually they shut up next door, we were just about to nod off when a light shone into our room like a plane was hurtling towards us. Didn't sleep much. Found out, after my husband complained about everything from the dangerous room, paper thin walls, light and the dribbling shower, that the light is in fact for our safety, it is a detector of movement to stop burglars (the fact is that it blinded us, so the burglar in fact has an advantage). Breakfast was awkward as we had it in their dining room. I asked for an omelette as I felt a bit sick and thought this may line my stomach, but she didn't know how to cook one so I opted for scrambled egg, which when presented to me, was cooked so much it actually would have passed as an omelette. We left after being mugged (well not mugged but it felt like it, paying seventy bloody quid for that stay). Seven thousand bags, I could have bought with that!

Day 14 as Mr and Mrs

The next place we stayed at was a lovely castle and we had a lovely big room. In the lounge area they had an open fire place, it was absolutely perfect. Then it was time for dinner. The starter was perfect and so was the wine, but the main, oh my God! I asked the waitress (who I thought was a waiter) if I could have a steak knife for my duck as it was a bit tough, and the waitress bellowed in her thick Scottish accent, "*OUR KNIVES ARE'LL ADEQUATE YOOOO DOOOOOOO NOT NEED OR WANT AEEE STEAK KNIFE."*

I can safely say we didn't have or need a steak knife and we didn't have a dessert either, we scarpered to the bar for a few stiff whiskeys by the roaring fire instead! We made it to bed without being murdered by the waitress/ waiter but we didn't sleep much because we were convinced we could hear people trying to break into our room.

Day 15 as Mr and Mrs

Well, it's now seven thirty and we can go down for breakfast, I have been awake since four thirty, couldn't sleep. Felt really sick, bloody whiskey. I am so tired and now feel slightly sketchy, I hope to God that the beast isn't serving breakfast! We went down, heads held high, and my husband held me back and said, "Our friend is serving breakfast." I just wanted to cry. We both ordered a full English, it was lovely apart from the haggis. The waitress came over to clear our plates and looked me straight in the eye.*"SOMETHING WRONG WITH THEEEEEEE HAGGIS?"*

"No, no I am just so full up."

"YOUUUUUU HAVENT EVEN TRIED IT!" and swiped my plate away. Once she got to the kitchen, we legged it.

Day 16 as Mr and Mrs

We went to visit a lovely old castle today and joined up to

the National Trust as we love the history of England, and it will be a good excuse to go and visit all the sites and stay away more often. We were inside this stunning old building that a family still lived in, and my husband (I love saying that) was taking pictures of everything but me, his new wife! After about half an hour of him snapping away on his camera, a security guard came up to me and asked me why he was taking pictures of the old locks on the door and windows. I explained that he loves old furniture and fixings and that we live in a very old house, the security guard then looked relieved and said, "Oh, ha ha, I thought he was planning to burgle this place."

Great, better warn my family and friends that we may be appearing on Crimewatch very soon.

Day 17 as Mr and Mrs

I tell you, the sheep in Scotland are a bunch of hard bastards, they hang from the cliff edges and look like they want to kick you in the face with their massive hooves. They make our southern sheep look like a bunch of softies.

Day 18 as Mr and Mrs

We have travelled over two thousand, five hundred miles in two weeks in an Astra through England, Scotland and Wales. We have seen so many wonderful places. I am really glad to be home now but I am not looking forward to facing reality again. Feeling really tired, going to have an early night.

Day 19 as Mr and Mrs

OH MY GOD, I'M PREGNANT!

Lightning Source UK Ltd.
Milton Keynes UK
UKOW04f1152170914

238720UK00001B/40/P